ROCK & POP

Male Voi[cal]s

C000193469

VO[cal]s

8

ROCK & POP

TRINITY
COLLEGE LONDON

THE EXAM AT A GLANCE

For your Rock & Pop exam you will need to perform a set of **three songs** and one of the **Session skills** assessments, either **Playback** or **Improvising**. You can choose the order in which you play your set-list.

Song 1

Choose a song from this book

OR from www.trinityrock.com

Song 2

Choose a different song from this book

OR from www.trinityrock.com

OR perform a song you have chosen yourself: this could be your own cover version or a song you have written. It should be at the same level as the songs in this book. See the website for detailed requirements.

Song 3: Technical focus

Choose one of the Technical focus songs from this book, which cover three specific technical elements.

Session skills

Choose either **Playback** or **Improvising**.

When you are preparing for your exam please check on www.trinityrock.com for the most up-to-date information and requirements as these can change from time to time.

CONTENTS

Trinity College London's Rock & Pop syllabus and supporting publications have been devised and produced in association with Faber Music and Peters Edition London.

Trinity College London
Registered office:
89 Albert Embankment
London SE1 7TP UK
T + 44 (0)20 7820 6100
F + 44 (0)20 7820 6161
E music@trinitycollege.co.uk
www.trinitycollege.co.uk

Registered in the UK. Company no. 02683033
Charity no. 1014792
Patron HRH The Duke of Kent KG

Copyright © 2012 Trinity College London
First published in 2012 by Trinity College London

Cover and book design by Chloë Alexander
Brand development by Andy Ashburner @ Caffeinehit (www.caffeinehit.com)
Photographs courtesy of Rex Features Ltd
Printed in England by Caligraving Ltd

Audio produced, mixed and mastered by Tom Fleming
Backing tracks arranged by Tom Fleming & Danny Gluckstein
Musicians
Vocals: Bo Walton, Brendan Reilly & Alison Symons
Keyboards: Dave Maric
Guitar & Bass: Tom Fleming
Drums: George Double
Studio Engineer: Joel Davies www.thelimehouse.com

All rights reserved

ISBN: 978-0-85736-262-9

SONGS DON'T STOP BELIEVIN'

Journey
Words and Music by Jonathan Cain, Neal Schon and Steve Perry

Just a ci-ty boy,_ born and raised in South De-troit,_

he took the mid-night train_ go-ing a-ny-where._

cresc.

49 (85)

F#/E · E · F#/E · Emaj7 · F#/B · B · F#/B · B

Street - lights, peo - ple,__ liv-ing just to find e - mo - tion,__

53 (89)

F#/E · E · F#/E · Emaj7 · F# F#sus4 B5 · *To Coda* ⊕ F# Bsus2 Eadd9

ff

hid - ing__ some - where in the night.__

57

B · F# · G#m7 · Eadd9

61

B *f* *Verse 2 improvise* · F# · G#m7 · Eadd9

2. Work-ing hard to get my fill, ev-'ry-bo - dy wants a thrill,

f

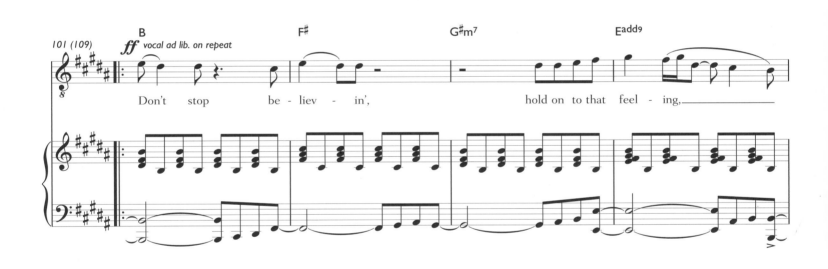

Don't stop be - liev - in', hold on to that feel - ing,

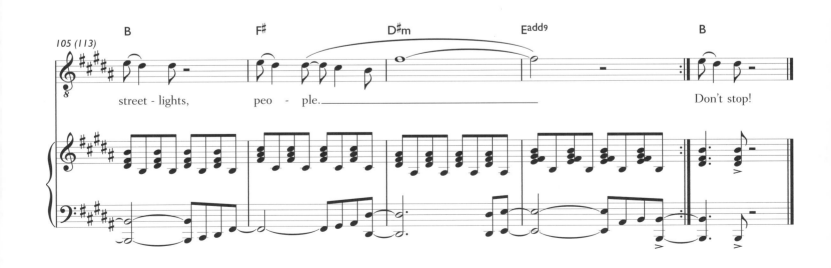

street - lights, peo - ple. Don't stop!

SONGS

JUST THE WAY YOU ARE (AMAZING)

Bruno Mars

Words and Music by Khalil Walton, Peter Hernandez, Philip Lawrence, Ari Levine and Khari Cain

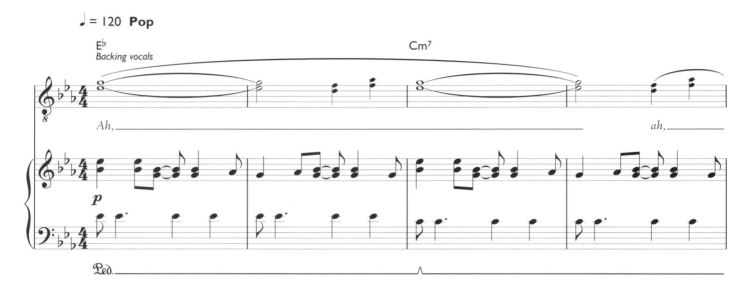

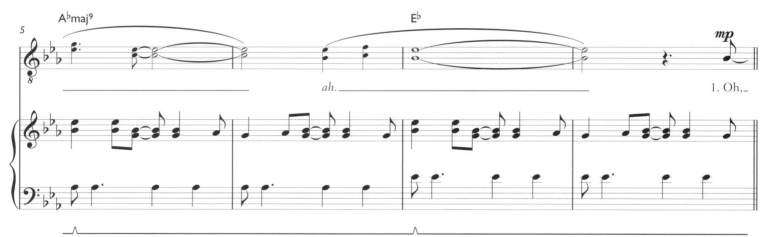

www.trinityrock.com

there's not a thing___ that I___ would change,___ 'cause you're a - maz-

- ing   just___ the___ way___ you   are.___   And when you   smile,___

___   the whole world stops___ and   stares for a   while,___   'cause girl, you're a - maz-

- ing_____   just___ the___ way___ you   are,___   yeah.___

SONGS BAT OUT OF HELL

Meat Loaf
Words and Music by Jim Steinman

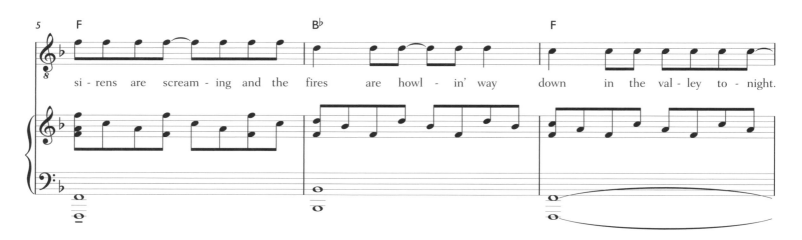

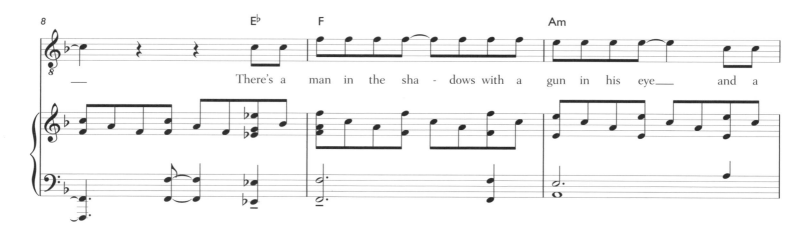

all a-bout to see the light. No-thing ev - er grows in this rot-ten old hole and

ev -'ry-thing is stun-ted and lost and no-thing real-ly rocks and no-

- thing real - ly rolls and no - thing's ev - er worth the cost.____

YOUR PAGE NOTES

SONGS

CRY ME A RIVER

Justin Timberlake
Words and Music by Timothy Mosley, Justin Timberlake and Scott Storch

♩ = 72 **R 'n' B**

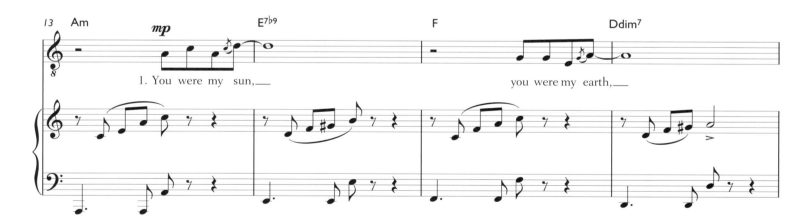

1. You were my sun,___ you were my earth,___

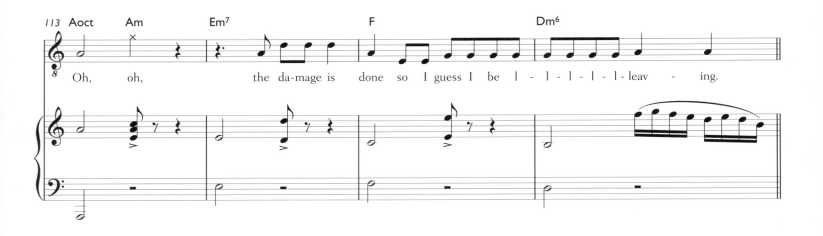

Oh, oh, the da-mage is done so I guess I be l-l-l-l-l-l-leav - ing.

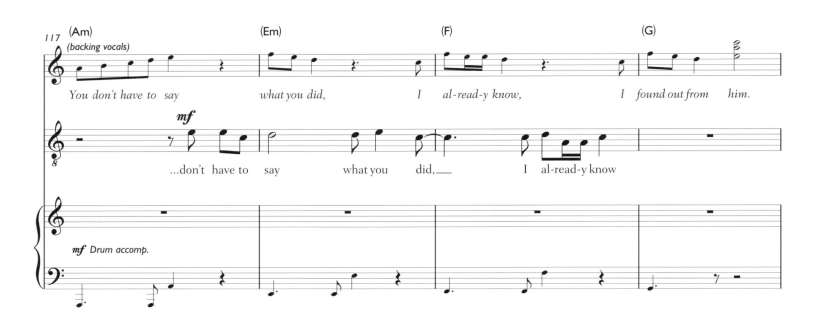

(backing vocals)

You don't have to say what you did, I al-read-y know, I found out from him.

...don't have to say what you did,___ I al-read-y know

mf Drum accomp.

Now there's just no chance for you and me, there'll ne-ver be, oo, cry me a riv -

no chance,___ you and me,___ and don't it make you sad a - bout

f vocal ad lib.

LILAC WINE

In your exam, you will be assessed on the following technical elements:

1 Long notes

Take care sustaining the long held notes, particularly in bars 16–19, and the high *pianissimo* in the final bar. These need good breath and tone control. Decide where to take a breath for the long held 'You' in bars 16–19. Colour the long notes (in, for example, bars 20–31 and 38–48) by starting the note straight and gradually adding *vibrato*.

2 Singing in a recitative style

The opening section and bars 32–37 are both marked 'freely' and should be sung in a recitative style, following the natural inflections, rhythms and tempo of speech. The rhythm in these passages can be quite free, but ensure that the first beat of each bar is in time and synchronises with the backing track. Aim to characterise atmospheric words such as 'cool' in bar 2 and 'misty' in bar 3.

3 Tonal variety across registers

The wide range of 'Lilac Wine' gives you scope to explore a variety of vocal tones in different registers of your voice. The song starts at a gentle *piano*, almost spoken, where you can use a softer, warmer tone. As the pitch gets higher and the song increases in volume you can experiment with different tone qualities and registers. For example, you could sing falsetto for the G on the word 'love' in bars 30–31 but then use a strong head voice for the G in bar 32.

LILAC WINE

Jeff Buckley
Words and Music by James Shelton

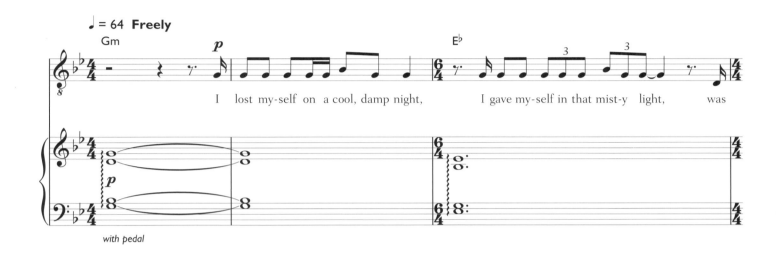

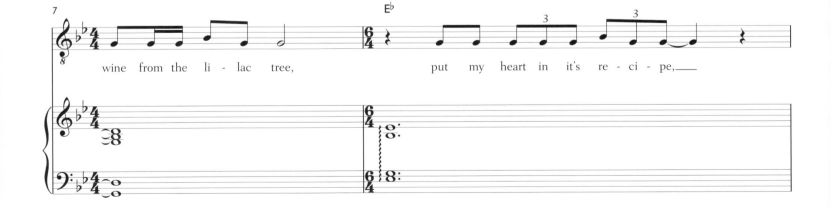

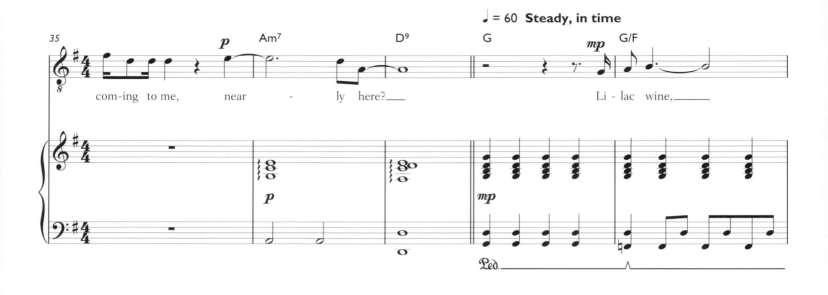

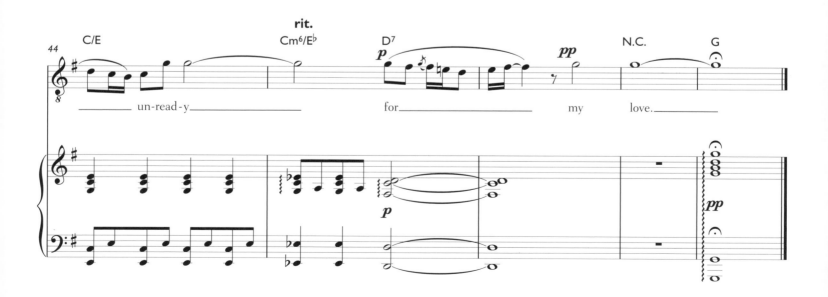

REET PETITE

In your exam, you will be assessed on the following technical elements:

1 Transition between different registers

'Reet Petite' mostly uses head voice, but also chest voice and falsetto. Aim for a smooth transition between registers, taking particular care with the transition from head voice to falsetto and back in bars 110–113. Falsetto can be tiring, so don't force it and avoid singing falsetto for too long.

2 Singing ad lib

There is an ad lib section in bars 86–109 – this is your opportunity to put your personal mark on the song. Remember, the demonstration track on the CD is a guide only: you should aim to develop your own version of this section. Practise singing it in a variety of ways – exploring different melodic, rhythmic and dynamic ideas – and decide what works best, while making sure that you follow the chord sequence. You could try using the pentatonic scale F, G, A, C, D.

3 Vocal bends (upward fall-offs)

There are upward vocal bends throughout this song. These are shown by the sign ✓ – in bars 9 and 13, for example. You should aim for clearly controlled *glissandi* between the two pitches – from the specified note to an ad lib pitch. Keep the bends light – they are almost 'throwaway' gestures. In the passage at bars 13–15, practise first without the slide until the pitches are secure, then add the upward fall-off – which changes from head voice to high falsetto.

REET PETITE

Jackie Wilson
Words and Music by Tyran Carlo and Berry Gordy Jr

oh,　　　　oh,___ oh, oh, oh.　　　　　Rrrr - - -

Reet Pe - tite,___ the fin-est girl you'll ev - er wan-na meet.　　　　　1. Well,　　have you

ev - er seen a girl for whom your soul you'd give, for whom you'd fight for, die for, pray___

(2.) fills her clothes, a from her head to toe, I want the world to know I

_41 (53)_   **F7**   **Bb6**

___ to God you'd lie   for? She's so_____ fine,_____ she's
love her, love her so.   She's al - - - - right,_____ she's

_44 (56)_   **F6**   **C7**   **Bb7**

so_____ fine,_____ she's real - ly sweet, the fin - est girl you ev - er wan - na
al - - right,_____ she's al - right, she loves_ me all the_ day and_

1.   **F6**   **2.**   **F6**   **N.C.**

_48_   _f_

meet.   2. Well,_ she real - ly night.   Oh, oh, oh,

ABOUT THE SONGS

DON'T STOP BELIEVIN'

Journey

Californian rock band Journey was formed in 1973 in San Francisco. The line-up included two former members of Santana – Neal Schon and Gregg Rolie. Over the years they frequently altered their musical approach and personnel, achieving most commercial success in the late 1970s and early 1980s. Lead singer Steve Perry grew up in California, the son of a vocalist. He played drums in his high school band and sang in the choir. His powerful voice is immediately identifiable with 1980s stadium rock.

The power ballad 'Don't Stop Believin" is taken from Journey's best-selling album *Escape* (1981). It is a timeless anthem and has been used in dozens of American sporting events as well as films and television programmes. There have been many covers of the song, notably by the cast of the American television series *Glee* in 2009.

The song has an odd structure: after the famous opening piano riff, the verses are separated by several different sections and the chorus only appears towards the end of the song. Co-writer and keyboards player Jonathan Cain said of the chorus: '. . . we knew we wanted to save it. It's like a wave about to happen – the anticipation of something happening, a change in your life'.

PERFORMANCE HINTS & TIPS

'Don't Stop Believin" has a strong narrative element, so make sure that you tell the story with clear diction, using bright vowels and crisp consonants. Try speaking the lyrics, first at a slower speed, articulating the consonants clearly (and not forgetting about the endings of words).

Make sure you plan where you are going to breathe. Short ideas make up longer phrases, so take care not to interrupt the melodic flow. There are several melismatic passages – where a group of notes is sung on one syllable. In bar 104, for example, the word 'feeling' is sung over six notes. Make sure you can pitch each note accurately at a slow tempo before gradually increasing the speed. Aim to move between the notes cleanly.

In the improvisation section (bars 61–76), you should stay within the feeling and style of the song. Base your ideas on music from earlier in the song – taking care to make the lyrics clear.

'Workin' hard to get my fill'

JUST THE WAY YOU ARE (AMAZING)

Bruno Mars

Bruno Mars, real name Peter Gene Hernandez, is a Filipino-Puerto Rican American singer-songwriter, producer and multi-instrumentalist. He grew up in Hawaii in a musical family as one of six siblings and fronted the family band from the age of four. At 17 he moved to Los Angeles and signed first to Motown Records and then to Atlantic Records. He became part of the successful music-writing and production trio The Smeezingtons and has co-written songs for Cee Lo Green, Alexandra Burke and Flo Rida – for whom he helped to pen the number one hit 'Right Round' in 2009. He also co-wrote the Sugababes' hit song 'Get Sexy'.

Bruno Mars' music is versatile and accessible, drawing on a wide variety of styles and incorporating elements of reggae and Motown. He often cites doo-wop music as a major influence – his eclectic debut album (in 2010) is titled *Doo Wops & Hooligans*. 'Just The Way You Are', the lead single from the album, is a feel-good R'n'B pop hit with optimistic and carefree lyrics.

PERFORMANCE · HINTS & TIPS

The fast tempo of 'Just The Way You Are' requires clear diction, especially in the syncopated passages. Use bright vowels and crisp consonants: try speaking the lyrics, first at a slower speed, articulating the consonants clearly (not forgetting about the endings of words). Put a slight emphasis on the syncopations on words such as 'eyes' in bar 9, and 'hair' in bar 11.

Aim to make confident and precise entries – you will need to count carefully to make sure that you come in at exactly the right place each time. Careful control of chest voice is needed in bars 8–23 and 41–47, and take care with the transition to head voice which follows both of these passages.

There is a melisma – where one syllable is sung across several notes – on the word 'say' in bar 55. Make sure you can pitch each note accurately at a slow tempo before gradually increasing the speed. Aim to move between the notes cleanly, without sliding over them.

'There's *not* a *thing* that *I* would *change*'

BAT OUT OF HELL

Meat Loaf

Meat Loaf (real name, Marvin Lee Addy) was born in Dallas, Texas. His early professional breaks came from acting in musicals, notably *Hair* and the film of *The Rocky Horror Show*. He eventually left the theatre to concentrate exclusively on music.

An exuberant performer, Meat Loaf achieved worldwide success with the grandiose concept album *Bat Out Of Hell* (1977). Co-written by Meat Loaf and his mentor Jim Steinman, this album has over-the-top excesses of rock, heavy metal and opera. The strong melodies and Meat Loaf's powerful vocals are enriched by top quality wall-of-sound production and a full orchestra. The album opens with the melodramatic title track – a song inspired by the teenage tragedy songs, such as 'Leader Of The Pack', that were popular in the 1950s and 1960s. Meat Loaf always performs 'Bat Out Of Hell' as the final song in his live concerts.

PERFORMANCE HINTS & TIPS

This melodramatic song is almost operatic in style. Make sure that your voice is thoroughly warmed up before tackling it. The dynamics need to be extreme and the high passages are all sung in head voice.

The fast sections are driven by the words and need a *marcato* – sometimes *staccato* – attack. Try speaking the words in rhythm before you sing the song in order to get the rhythms accurate. Articulate the consonants clearly – this will give the song energy and enable the listener to understand you more easily.

The passages in bars 59–63 and bars 64–68 should contrast dramatically: the first should be sung in head voice, *fortissimo* and *marcato*; the second passage should be sung *legato* with a much warmer, gentler tone.

Careful control is needed for the *rallentando* passages in bars 64, 67–68 and in the final section (bars 113–125). Take care to synchronise with the backing track.

'I'll come crawling on back to you'

CRY ME A RIVER

Justin Timberlake

Justin Timberlake grew up in Tennessee in a small community near Memphis, where his father was director of the local Baptist church choir. He has enjoyed a varied career as a musician, actor and businessman. His rise to fame began on The Disney Channel as part of the children's show *The Mickey Mouse Club*. Worldwide fame arrived in the late 1990s as a member of popular boy-band *NSYNC when Timberlake, the youngest member of the band, became a major celebrity and heartthrob.

Having co-written many of *NSYNC's singles, Timberlake launched a successful solo singing career in 2002 with the release of his first album *Justified*. The synth pop ballad 'Cry Me A River' features guest vocals from Timbaland, a prominent R'n'B producer. It showcases Timberlake's signature falsetto sound and has become one of his most famous songs. It is thought to have been written about the break-up from his celebrity girlfriend Britney Spears.

PERFORMANCE · HINTS & TIPS ·

'Cry Me A River' should be sung with rhythmic precision. Listen to Justin Timberlake's version and notice how he sings it very precisely in time. This is particularly important in passages such as bars 77–83, where you have to synchronise with the backing vocals. Your diction needs to be crisp at this fast tempo, especially in the ♪ passages (in bars 25 and 79, for example).

Make sure you know where you are going to breathe. Short ideas make up longer phrases, so take care not to interrupt the melodic flow by breathing too often, or in the wrong places. Breathe through the longer sections in, for example, bars 13–16 and 21–24.

The vocal ad libs in the final section provide an opportunity to put your personal mark on the song. Practise singing it in a variety of ways – exploring different melodic, rhythmic and dynamic ideas – and decide what works best, while making sure that you follow the chord sequence. You could try using the minor pentatonic scale A, B, C, E, G.

'*Now* it's *your* turn *to* cry'

LILAC WINE

Jeff Buckley

Californian Jeff Buckley (1966–1997) was the son of musical parents: his mother was a classical cellist and pianist while his father was the singer-songwriter Tim Buckley. He started to learn guitar when he was five and played electric guitar in the high school jazz band. He later went to music college and made a living singing in New York clubs and bars. He first came to major public attention when, as a young boy, he sang at a memorial service for his father who had died of a drug overdose at the age of 28. Buckley had a versatile singing voice with a multi-octave range.

'Lilac Wine' originally dates from 1950. It is one of three covers taken from Buckley's only studio album *Grace*. As well as several well-crafted original songs, this eclectic album includes a setting of Benjamin Britten's 'Corpus Christi Carol' and what many consider to be the definitive version of the Leonard Cohen song 'Hallelujah'. There have been several covers of the powerful ballad 'Lilac Wine' by, amongst others, Nina Simone, Elkie Brooks and Imelda May.

PERFORMANCE · HINTS & TIPS

This song has many wide leaps: for example the octave leap in bars 9–10; the minor seventh in bars 13–14; and the minor sixth in bars 12–13. Practise these carefully until the intonation is entirely secure. The changes between E♮ and E♭ in bars 12–15 also need careful pitching.

There are several melismatic passages – where a group of notes is sung on one syllable. In bars 43–44, for example, the word 'feel' is sung over six notes. Make sure you can pitch each note accurately at a slow tempo before gradually increasing the speed. Aim to move between the notes cleanly.

'*I* lost *myself* on *a* cool, *damp* night'

REET PETITE

Jackie Wilson

Jackie Wilson (1934–1984) was raised in a Detroit ghetto. As a teenager, he had a promising career as a boxer but gave it up to become a singer. He was a powerful vocalist and an electrifying showman famous for his soaring dramatic vocals, dazzling footwork and stamina. He was a well-known R'n'B performer with Billy Ward & The Dominoes before he became a soloist in the 1950s: his recordings were important in the transition from R'n'B to soul. Over the years, he recorded a string of hits in a variety of styles including doo-wop, R'n'B, pop and soul. Wilson's life was beset by tragedy. He was shot and seriously wounded in 1961 and in 1975 he collapsed of a heart attack on stage and never fully recovered. He died in 1984.

'Reet Petite' (1957), Jackie Wilson's first solo hit, has elements of R'n'B and soul, as well as a touch of rock 'n' roll. It was co-written by the then little-known Berry Gordy Jr, who later founded the soul music label Tamla Motown.

'Reet Petite' should be sung with energy, a strong sense of rhythm and a feeling of fun. The lyrics need to be clearly enunciated: you could exaggerate the consonant sounds L, K and B in bars 6–7 and 10–11. Experiment with changes of articulation in, for example, bars 22–23, 29–32 and 38–49.

Emphasise the words 'She's so fine' (bars 42–45) by singing them *legato*, to contrast with the shorter sounds used throughout much of the song. To master the rolled Rrr's (in bar 33, for example), it will help to listen to Jackie Wilson or the demo track and imitate the sound.

'She's *like* honey *from a bee*'

PLAYBACK

For your exam, you can choose either Playback or Improvising (see page 56). If you choose Playback, you will be asked to perform some music you have not seen or heard before.

In the exam, you will be given the song chart and the examiner will play a recording of the music. You will hear several four-bar to eight-bar phrases on the recording: you should sing each of them straight back in turn. There's a rhythm track going throughout, which helps you keep in time. There should not be any gaps in the music.

In the exam you will have two chances to perform with the recording:
- First time – for practice
- Second time – for assessment.

You should listen to the audio, copying what you hear; you can also read the music. Here are some practice song charts which are also on the CD in this book. The music is printed without text and may be sung to any vowel (with or without consonant) or to sol-fa. Some of the examples may include accents so you may need to use consonants or scat words for these to make them really obvious.

Don't forget that the Playback test can include requirements which may not be shown in these examples, including those from earlier grades. Check the parameters at www.trinityrock.com to prepare for everything which might come up in your exam.

'I really *like* the *way* music *looks* on *paper.* It *looks* like *art* to *me*'

Steve Vai

Practice playback 1

Practice playback 2

SESSION SKILLS

IMPROVISING

For your exam, you can choose either Playback (see page 53), or Improvising. If you choose to improvise, you will be asked to improvise over a backing track that you haven't heard before in a specified style.

In the exam, you will be given a song chart and the examiner will play a recording of the backing track. The backing track consists of a passage of music played on a loop. You should improvise a melody line over the backing track.

In the exam you will have two chances to perform with the recording:
- First time – for practice
- Second time – for assessment.

Here are some improvising charts for practice which are also on the CD in this book. The music is printed without text and may be sung to any vowel (with or without consonant) or to sol-fa.

Don't forget that the Improvising test can include requirements which may not be shown in these examples, including those from earlier grades. Check the parameters at www.trinityrock.com to prepare for everything which might come up in your exam.

Practice improvisation 1

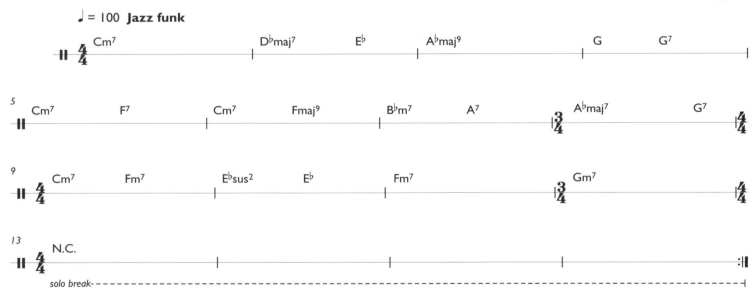

Practice improvisation 2

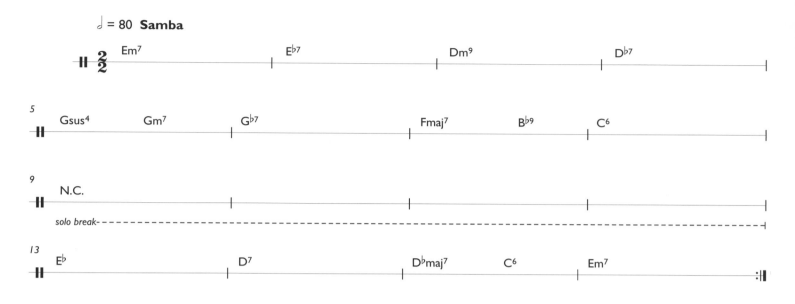

♩ = 80 **Samba**

| Em⁷ | E♭⁷ | Dm⁹ | D♭⁷ |

5
| Gsus⁴ | Gm⁷ | G♭⁷ | Fmaj⁷ | B♭⁹ | C⁶ |

9
| N.C. | | | |
solo break

13
| E♭ | D⁷ | D♭maj⁷ | C⁶ | Em⁷ |

'Relax.
Enjoy yourself.
Play *a lot.*'

Joe Satriani

CHOOSING A SONG FOR YOUR EXAM

There are lots of options to help you choose your three songs for the exam. For Songs 1 and 2, you can choose a song which is:

- from this book
- from www.trinityrock.com

Or for Song 2 you can choose a song which is:

- sheet music from a printed or online source.
- your own arrangement of a song or a song you have written yourself.

You can perform the song unaccompanied or with a backing track (minus the solo voice). If you like, you can create a backing track yourself (or with friends).

For Grade 8, the song should last between two-and-a-half and four minutes, and the level of difficulty should be similar to your other songs. When choosing a song, think about:

- Does it work for my voice?
- Are there any technical elements that are too difficult for me?
- Do I enjoy singing it?
- Does it work with my other pieces to create a good set-list?

See www.trinityrock.com for further information and advice on choosing your own song.

SHEET MUSIC

For your exam, you must always bring an original copy of the book or download sheets with email certificate / proof of purchase for each song you perform in the exam. If you choose to write your own song you must provide the examiner with a copy of your music.

Your music can be:

- a lead sheet with lyrics, chords and melody line
- a chord chart with lyrics
- a full score using conventional staff notation

The title of the song and your name should be on the sheet music.

IMPROVISING IN SONGS

Improvisation is an exciting and creative way to make the music your own. This might include singing your own melody line or ad-libbing around a given tune. Rock and pop music often includes opportunities for musicians to improvise during a song – this is a great way to display your vocal skills and musical abilities.

Make sure you know the song well and feel comfortable and confident with the rhythms, chord progressions and the general groove that underpins the music. Once you're familiar with it, the best way to learn how to improvise is to do it!

Some useful starting points might be:

- Identify just a few notes that sound good over the chord progressions, and experiment with these first.
- Add more notes as your musical ideas start to develop – improvising is often most effective when a simple idea is repeated, varied and extended.
- You don't need to fill every gap! Silence can be an important – and very effective – part of your improvisation.
- The more you improvise – and experiment – the better you will become, until your improvisations seem effortless.

It's important to be aware of the tonality of the song and to recognise different scales and modes that are appropriate to use. Start by familiarising yourself with:

- the minor pentatonic scale
- the blues scale
- the Dorian mode
- major and minor scales

You might find it useful to listen to some original versions of different rock and pop songs. Have a go at learning some vocal solos in these versions – this will help you to develop an understanding of how other musicians develop musical material.

PERFORMING

Being well prepared is the secret of a good performance. The more you practise, the better you will perform.

Top Ten Practice Tips

1 Develop a regular practice routine. Try to set aside a certain amount of time every day.

2 Choose specific things to practise each week.

3 Set goals for each practice session and continually review your progress.

4 Sing a wide variety of songs – not just your favourites over and over again – to increase your skill and adaptability.

5 Identify the parts of the songs you find difficult and give them special attention.

6 Practise those techniques that you struggle with as well as those you find easier.

7 Don't reinforce mistakes by repeating them over and over again.

8 Include warm-ups and technical exercises in your practice sessions as well as songs.

9 Use a metronome.

10 Record yourself on audio or video. Listen to your older recordings to see how much you have improved.

Try to memorise the music – aim to sound free and natural and put your own stamp on the songs.

PERFORMING

BEFORE YOUR PERFORMANCE

- Watch and listen to others perform. Go to live performances and watch some videos online. Think about the aspects of performances you particularly like and try them out.
- Practise singing in front of an audience and communicate with them.
- Learn some relaxation and breathing exercises.
- Be positive about your performance. Think about how good your performance will be.
- Know your music.

ON THE DAY OF YOUR PERFORMANCE

- Wear something comfortable.
- Try some physical exercises.
- Warm up.
- Do some relaxation and breathing exercises.

THE PERFORMANCE

Your audience may be large or small – and in an exam may only be one person – but it is important to give a sense of performance no matter how many people are present.

- Walk into the room confidently.
- Keep your head up, so you can look at your audience and acknowledge them.
- Focus on the music.
- Look confident and keep going, no matter what happens.
- Engage with your audience.
- Enjoy yourself.

MICROPHONE TECHNIQUE

Here are some points to bear in mind when you use a mic in performance:

- Consider whether you are going to hold the mic or use a stand. If you use a stand, place it at a comfortable height so you don't have to bend over. Be aware of trailing leads.
- There should be about five to eight centimetres between your mouth and the mic – closer for quiet, breathy singing and further away for louder singing and powerful high notes.

- Experiment with different vocal sounds – whispering and shouting, high and low notes, vowels and consonants. Learn how to avoid hisses and pops. Depending on the mic you use, popping sounds can occur when singing P, B, T and D and hissing sounds on S and Z.
- Never point the mic towards a speaker or stage monitor – this will create feedback.

YOUR PAGE NOTES

PERFORMING WITH BACKING TRACKS

The CD contains demos and backing tracks of all the songs in the book. The additional songs at www.trinityrock.com also come with demos and backing tracks.

- In your exam, you can perform with the backing track or create your own.
- The backing tracks begin with a click track, which sets the tempo and helps you start accurately.
- Be careful to balance the volume of the backing track against your voice.
- Listen carefully to the backing track to ensure you are playing in time.

If you are creating your own backing track here are some further tips:
- Make sure the sound quality is of a good standard.
- Think carefully about the instruments/sounds you are putting on the backing track.
- Avoid copying what you are singing on the backing track – it should support not duplicate.
- Do you need to include a click track at the beginning?

COPYRIGHT IN A SONG

If you are a singer or songwriter it is important to know about copyright. When someone writes a song or creates an arrangement they own the copyright (sometimes called 'the rights') to that version. The copyright means that other people cannot copy it, sell it, perform it in a concert, make it available online or record it without the owner's permission or the appropriate licence. When you write a song you automatically own the copyright to it, which means that other people cannot copy your work. But just as importantly, you cannot copy other people's work, or perform it in public without their permission or the appropriate licence.

Points to remember
- You can create a cover version of a song for an exam or other non-public performance.
- You cannot record your cover version and make your recording available to others (by copying

it or uploading it to a website) without the appropriate licence.
- You own the copyright of your own original song, which means that no one is allowed to copy it.
- You cannot copy someone else's song without their permission or the appropriate licence.
- If you would like to use somebody else's words in your own song you must check if they are in copyright and, if so, we recommend you confirm with the author that they are happy for the words to be used as lyrics.
- Materials protected by copyright can normally be used as lyrics in our examinations as these are private performances under copyright law. The examiner may ask you the name of the original author in the exam.
- When you present your own song to the examiner make sure you include the title, the names of any writers and the source of your lyrics.

ALSO AVAILABLE

Trinity College London Rock & Pop examinations 2012-2017 are also available for:

Bass Initial
ISBN: 978-0-85736-227-8

Bass Grade 1
ISBN: 978-0-85736-228-5

Bass Grade 2
ISBN: 978-0-85736-229-2

Bass Grade 3
ISBN: 978-0-85736-230-8

Bass Grade 4
ISBN: 978-0-85736-231-5

Bass Grade 5
ISBN: 978-0-85736-232-2

Bass Grade 8
ISBN: 978-0-85736-233-9

Bass Grade 7
ISBN: 978-0-85736-234-6

Bass Grade 8
ISBN: 978-0-85736-235-3

Keyboards Initial
ISBN: 978-0-85736-236-0

Keyboards Grade 1
ISBN: 978-0-85736-237-7

Keyboards Grade 2
ISBN: 978-0-85736-238-4

Keyboards Grade 3
ISBN: 978-0-85736-239-1

Keyboards Grade 4
ISBN: 978-0-85736-240-7

Keyboards Grade 5
ISBN: 978-0-85736-241-4

Keyboards Grade 8
ISBN: 978-0-85736-242-1

Keyboards Grade 7
ISBN: 978-0-85736-243-8

Keyboards Grade 8
ISBN: 978-0-85736-244-5

Drums Initial
ISBN: 978-0-85736-245-2

Drums Grade 1
ISBN: 978-0-85736-246-9

Drums Grade 2
ISBN: 978-0-85736-247-6

Drums Grade 3
ISBN: 978-0-85736-248-3

Drums Grade 4
ISBN: 978-0-85736-249-0

Drums Grade 5
ISBN: 978-0-85736-250-6

Drums Grade 8
ISBN: 978-0-85736-251-3

Drums Grade 7
ISBN: 978-0-85736-252-0

Drums Grade 8
ISBN: 978-0-85736-253-7

Vocals Initial
ISBN: 978-0-85736-254-4

Vocals Grade 1
ISBN: 978-0-85736-255-1

Vocals Grade 2
ISBN: 978-0-85736-256-8

Vocals Grade 3
ISBN: 978-0-85736-257-5

Vocals Grade 4
ISBN: 978-0-85736-258-2

Vocals Grade 5
ISBN: 978-0-85736-259-9

Vocals Grade 8 (female voice)
ISBN: 978-0-85736-263-6

Vocals Grade 8 (male voice)
ISBN: 978-0-85736-260-5

Vocals Grade 7 (female voice)
ISBN: 978-0-85736-264-3

Vocals Grade 7 (male voice)
ISBN: 978-0-85736-261-2

Vocals Grade 8 (female voice)
ISBN: 978-0-85736-265-0

Vocals Grade 8 (male voice)
ISBN: 978-0-85736-262-9

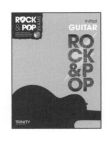

Guitar Initial
ISBN: 978-0-85736-218-6

Guitar Grade 1
ISBN: 978-0-85736-219-3

Guitar Grade 2
ISBN: 978-0-85736-220-9

Bass Grade 8
ISBN: 978-0-85736-221-6

Guitar Grade 4
ISBN: 978-0-85736-222-3

Guitar Grade 5
ISBN: 978-0-85736-223-0

Guitar Grade 8
ISBN: 978-0-85736-224-7

Guitar Grade 7
ISBN: 978-0-85736-225-4

Guitar Grade 8
ISBN: 978-0-85736-226-1